Persephone

and the
Pomegranate Seeds

First published in 2008 by
Franklin Watts
338 Euston Road
London
NW1 3BH

Franklin Watts Australia
Level 17/207 Kent Street
Sydney
NSW 2000

A CIP catalogue record for this book is available
from the British Library.

ISBN 978 0 7496 7995 8 (hbk)
ISBN 978 0 7496 8003 9 (pbk)

Series Editor: Melanie Palmer
Series Advisor: Dr Barrie Wade
Series Designer: Peter Scoulding

Printed in China

Franklin Watts is a division of
Hachette Children's Books,
an Hachette Livre UK company
www.hachettelivre.co.uk

HOPSCOTCH
MYTHS

Persephone

and the
Pomegranate Seeds

by Maggie Moore and Martin Impey

W

FRANKLIN WATTS
LONDON•SYDNEY

Demeter was the goddess of
everything that grew on Earth.

Her daughter, Persephone, was beautiful. All the gods admired her. She helped her mother to cover the Earth with plants and flowers.

One day, Persephone was out
picking flowers for her mother.

At the same time, the god Hades
went out for a ride in his chariot.

As soon as Hades saw Persephone, he fell in love. He grabbed her and sped back down to his kingdom in the underworld.

"Welcome to the underworld," said Hades. "Now you must stay here and be my queen."

Persephone stamped her foot.

"No, I won't," she yelled.

"My mother needs me on Earth."

The underworld was cold, dark and
lonely. Persephone missed the warm,
bright sun and her friends on Earth.

"I know you miss the Earth,"
said Hades. "If you eat some of
this fruit, you will feel better."

But Persephone refused.

She was too sad to eat.

Back on Earth, Demeter looked everywhere for Persephone.

No one had seen her, not even the shepherd. She was so sad that she forgot to look after the plants and they started to die.

Soon there were no flowers. There
was no fruit and no corn. The
people on Earth began to starve.

Zeus, king of the gods, saw that the
Earth was bare. He sent Hermes,
his messenger, to find Persephone.

In the underworld, Hades tried once more to make Persephone eat. He knew that if she did, she would have to stay with him forever.

"Please eat this pomegranate," he begged her. "If you do, you can see your mother again," he lied.

So Persephone ate just four
of the pomegranate seeds.
"At last!" cried Hades, dancing
with joy. "Now you must stay here!"

Just then Hermes arrived, but he
was too late. "Don't eat anything
else!" he cried. Then he rushed
back to tell Demeter.

Demeter was furious. "Nothing will grow on Earth while Persephone is in the underworld," she told Zeus, angrily.

So Zeus thought of a plan. He sent
Hermes to bring Persephone to him.

"As you have eaten four seeds,
you must stay in the underworld
for four months each year,"
Zeus told Persephone.

"But for the other months of the
year, you can be with me on Earth,"
said her mother, Demeter.

So each year, when Persephone returns to the Earth, plants grow and corn ripens in the summer sun.

But when she goes down to the underworld, plants freeze in winter's cold. Nothing grows until her return and the start of spring.

Hopscotch has been specially designed to fit the requirements of the Literacy Framework. It offers real books by top authors and illustrators for children developing their reading skills. There are 63 Hopscotch stories to choose from:

* hardback